WiKIDly
Awesome Travels

An activity book
for kids exploring London

www.wikidly.com

ISBN: 978-0-9862375-1-5

Edited by Daphne Parsekian
Design by Elizabeth Gauthier
Images from Metro Creative Graphics

First Edition

We—Miranda McPhee and Suzanne Lifson—first met in Paris in 1990.

We have both been traveling since we were very young, and between us we have globetrotted to 35 different countries. We would like to say a huge thanks to our families and friends who helped create this book and gave us ideas, feedback, and encouragement. We made every effort to make sure the content of this activity book is accurate.

Visit us at www.wikidly.com

Contents

How to Use This Book

Hello! This WiKIDly Awesome Travels activity book puts you in the heart of London. Whether this is your first or tenth visit to London, this activity book will help you explore, think, learn, discover, and show how creative and artistic you are.

Before your trip, look at all of the great places you can go. London has a long and rich history stretching way back to before the Romans. During your visit, you'll hear many stories about kings and queens, heroes and villains, and traitors and saints along the way. There is so much to see here that you probably won't see it all in one visit, but you are sure to want to come back.

When you are in London, over breakfast each day, look through your book and talk about what you are going to explore that day. While out seeing the sights, test yourself with the quizzes, learn some funky facts you can share with your family and friends, and draw like an artist. Before bed each night, talk about where you've been, finish your drawings, and dream about the next day's adventures. End your trip by filling in your own London story.

Travel Information

Name of WIKIDly Awesome Traveler
_____

Date my WIKIDly Awesome Travels to London began
_____

The people I am traveling with
_____

Number of days we are spending in London
_____

Number of miles between my hometown and London
_____

Funky Fact

London has been the capital city for 2,000 years, since the Romans established it as Londinium.

Where are you?

When you get to London, look at a city map to find out where you are. Use the map during your stay to see where you are going and how you will get there.

- What do you think of London so far?

How is London different from where you live?

First Impressions

8

Quick Quiz

1

What is the subway in London called?
a) The Tube
b) The sub hub
c) The U-train

2

What color are mailboxes in London?
a) Red
b) Yellow
c) Blue

3

What do you call a bus with two levels?
a) A high roller
b) A double-decker
c) A super-bus

4

London taxi cabs, for the most part, are what color?
a) Blue
b) Black
c) Yellow

Funky Fact

A blue plaque (disc) on the front of a building means a famous person once worked or lived there.

Memorize the name of the hotel and street where you are staying.

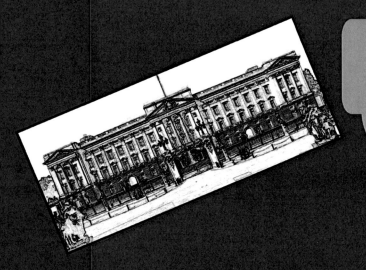

Funky Fact

More than 50,000 guests are invited to Buckingham Palace each year: royalty, politicians, and movie and sports stars as well as all kinds of people who have done good deeds.

History Bits

This building was originally a house that King George III bought in 1761. It was transformed into a palace in 1826. It is the Queen's official London residence, so she lives, works, and entertains here.

Is the Queen at Home?

When the Queen is "in residence" (living) at Buckingham Palace, you will see her Royal Standard (flag) flying above the Palace.

Draw one of the sentries and a sentry box.

Quick Quiz

1

What should you do if you meet the Queen?
a) Bow or curtsy
b) Salute
c) Shake her hand

2

The memorial in front of the palace is named after which queen?
a) Mary
b) Anne
c) Victoria

3

There are two parks in front of the palace—Green Park and which other?
a) St. John's
b) St. James's
c) St. Mark's

Check off what you saw.

☐ Changing the Guard Ceremony

☐ Balcony   ☐ Drawing Rooms

☐ Throne Room   ☐ State Dining Room

☐ Grand Staircase   ☐ Gold State Coach

☐ Diamond Jubilee State Coach

Funky Fact

More than 3,300 people are buried or commemorated in this Abbey.

History Bits

King Edward the Confessor turned an abbey into a church in 1065. King Henry III then started rebuilding it in 1245. It is called an abbey because it is a church with buildings where monks and nuns used to live. Coronations, royal weddings, state funerals, and regular services take place here.

The Grave of the Unknown Warrior

The body of a British soldier killed in France in World War I lies in this grave. We do not know his name or whether he was in the Army, Navy, or Air Force. This memorial represents all those who gave their lives for Britain but have no other memorial or grave.

Draw the Abbey here.

Quick Quiz

1

What is the mosaic behind the High Altar a scene of?
a) Easter
b) The Last Supper
c) Christmas

2

What is the Cosmati Pavement?
a) A blue stone
b) A mosaic floor
c) A carpet

3

What shape is Chapter House?
a) Octagonal
b) Round
c) Square

Check off what you saw.

☐ Shrine of St. Edward the Confessor

☐ Coronation Chair   ☐ Lady Chapel

☐ Poet's Corner   ☐ Quire

☐ Tomb of Elizabeth I   ☐ Cloisters

Funky Fact

The bell in the clock tower is commonly called Big Ben. In 2012 the clock tower was named the Elizabeth Tower to celebrate Queen Elizabeth's 60th year on the throne.

History Bits

This huge building is officially called the Palace of Westminster because a palace originally stood here. Since the 13th century, two sets of people ("Houses") have met here to make laws ("Parliament")—so this building is known as the Houses of Parliament.

Name these statues of famous people in Parliament Square:

1

The British Prime Minister during World War II leaning on a walking stick

2

The President of the United States standing in front of a chair

NOV 5

Guy Fawkes and the Gunpowder Plot

Draw Big Ben here.

In 1605 a group of traitors tried to kill King James I by blowing up the Houses of Parliament. Guy Fawkes was the one in charge of guarding the gunpowder. The plot was discovered, and the men were executed for treason. To celebrate the failure of the plot, bonfires and fireworks are lit across the country every year on November 5, which is called Guy Fawkes Day.

The leader of independence in India wearing glasses

The President of South Africa standing opposite Westminster Abbey

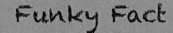

Funky Fact

Only the Queen may drive through Horse Guards Arch to the parade ground without showing a special pass to the sentries.

History Bits

The Household Cavalry Mounted Regiment in Horse Guards are soldiers on horseback. The troopers are part of the British Army. They also protect the Queen, and they play a big role in State Ceremonies.

Horse Guards Parade

In the 16th century this site was used for jousting tournaments. Two knights dressed in armor, riding horses, and carrying shields and lances (long poles) galloped towards each other and tried to knock each other off using their lances. Today this site is used for royal birthday celebrations and military ceremonies.

Draw the headdress worn by the mounted trooper at Horse Guards.

1

Who lives at 10 Downing Street?
a) The President
b) The Queen
c) The Prime Minister

2

What is sculpted on the Women of World War II Memorial?
a) Clothing
b) Flowers
c) Faces

Quick Quiz

3

What does a mounted sentry at Horse Guards hold in the left hand?
a) A sword
b) The reins
c) A pistol

4

What is a cenotaph?
a) A monument
b) A church
c) A statue

Funky Fact

Up in the Whispering Gallery, your whisper against the wall can be heard on the other side of the gallery, 112 feet away.

History Bits

The very first St. Paul's was founded in 604 AD. The current cathedral was designed by the architect Sir Christopher Wren after the Great Fire destroyed most of London in 1666.

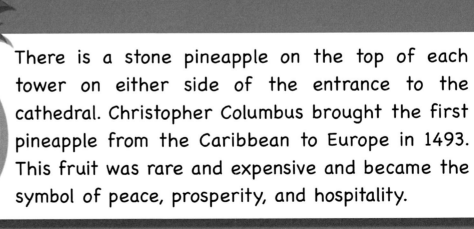

There is a stone pineapple on the top of each tower on either side of the entrance to the cathedral. Christopher Columbus brought the first pineapple from the Caribbean to Europe in 1493. This fruit was rare and expensive and became the symbol of peace, prosperity, and hospitality.

Draw St. Paul's Cathedral here.

Quick Quiz

1

What do you find in the crypt?
a) Tombs
b) Paintings
c) Jewels

2

What is the Light of the World?
a) A lamp
b) A statue
c) A painting

3

What are Great Tom and Great Paul?
a) Bells
b) Statues
c) Tombs

Check off what you saw.

☐ Dome   ☐ Golden Gallery

☐ Nave   ☐ High Altar

☐ Whispering Gallery   ☐ American Memorial Chapel

Trafalgar Square

Funky Fact

This is the largest square in London and has been a place for meetings, festivities, and demonstrations for hundreds of years.

Quick Quiz

1

Trafalgar Square is named after—
a) A battle
b) A general
c) A town

2

Admiral Horatio Nelson had only one eye. He also had only one—
a) Foot
b) Leg
c) Arm

3

What is St. Martin-in-the-Fields?
a) A statue
b) A church
c) A theater

History Bits

For centuries, most of this area was the courtyard for the royal mews (this is where horses are kept in stables, and people live upstairs). It was redesigned as a cultural area open to the public in 1812.

Covent Garden gets its name from a convent garden that was originally on this site.

History Bits

This area was a trading place called Lundenwic (or London market) back in the sixth century. It became an open-air fruit and vegetable market, and the piazza (public square) was created in 1631. It was modernized in 1974, and today it is full of shops, restaurants, and street performers.

Count the pillars on the Royal Opera House.

Discover how people used to travel at the London Transport Museum.

Watch the street performers on the piazza.

The London Eye is a giant observation wheel that takes 30 minutes to go around. See the famous sights of London from your capsule.

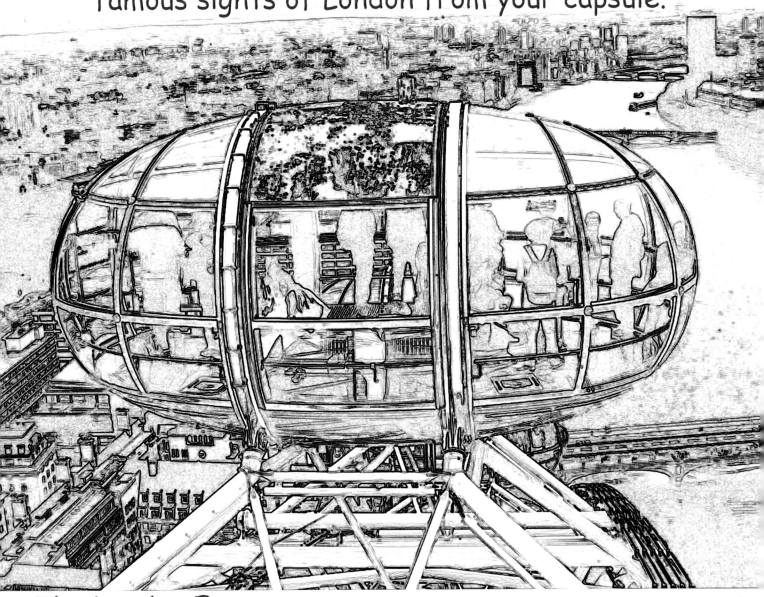

The London Eye

Along the Thames Quiz

1

Fill in the blank: The obelisk with Egyptian carvings on the Embankment is called "_____'s Needle."

a) Delilah
b) Caesar
c) Cleopatra

4

The Millennium Bridge is only for what?
a) Pedestrians
b) Trains
c) Cars

2 What is the purpose of the Thames Barrier?
a) To keep boats safe
b) To prevent flooding in London
c) To stop people from swimming

3

What is HMS Belfast?
a) A World War I warship
b) A submarine
c) A World War II warship

5

How many arches are there under Westminster Bridge?
a) Five
b) Seven
c) Eight

Legend says that if the ravens that permanently live in the Tower of London ever leave, the kingdom will fall.

History Bits

This castle was founded in 1066 by William the Conqueror. For hundreds of years, kings, queens, traitors, and sinners were imprisoned and put to death here. Today it is a Historic Royal Palace and houses the Crown Jewels.

Yeomen Warders

Yeomen Warders wear colorful, traditional uniforms and provide a ceremonial guard for the Tower. For more than 700 years, they have performed the "Ceremony of the Keys" every night to lock the gates and make sure the Tower is secure. Yeomen Warders are popularly called "Beefeaters," supposedly because they were allowed to eat a lot of beef. (But it's not polite to call them beefeaters when you talk to them.)

Draw your own Yeoman Warder here.

Quick Quiz

1

What used to take place on Tower Green?
a) Concerts
b) Sports
c) Executions

2

Why do kings and queens wear crowns?
a) To keep warm
b) To be seen easily
c) To show off

3

How many ravens must there always be living at the Tower?
a) Two
b) Four
c) Six

Check off what you saw.

☐ White Tower

☐ Crown Jewels

☐ Wakefield Tower

☐ Line of Kings

☐ Medieval Palace

Tower Bridge

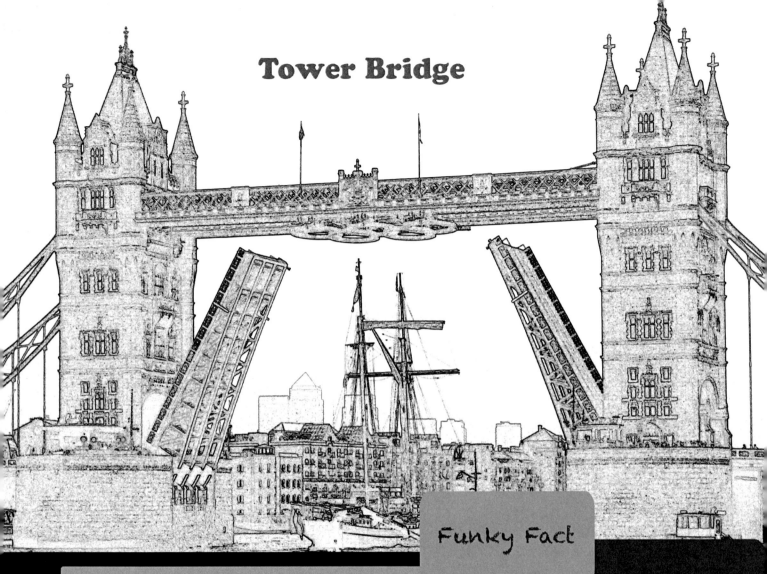

Funky Fact

The walkway over the bridge has a glass floor so you can see straight down to the road and the River Thames, 138 feet below.

History Bits

This bridge opened in 1894, and the road is split into two halves. When very tall ships need to go through, the traffic stops and the bridge opens upwards in the middle.

Shakespeare's Globe Theatre

Funky Fact

The first theatre burned down in 1613 due to an accident with a cannon during one of the plays.

History Bits

This theater is a reconstruction of two theaters built in 1599 and 1614. Plays written by William Shakespeare are performed live in the open air, and there are no spotlights or microphones.

Quick Quiz

1

Shakespeare was called the "Bard of Avon" because he lived in Avon. A bard is-
a) An author
b) A poet
c) A comic

2

What did spectators in the center of the arena have to do?
a) Stand
b) Kneel
c) Act

3

How many sides does this theater have?
a) Eight
b) Fourteen
c) Twenty

Funky Fact

The Round Pond is actually a rectangle that has rounded corners.

History Bits

Kensington Palace was designed by Sir Christopher Wren in 1689. Members of the royal family have homes and offices here. The Gardens are one of eight Royal Parks in London that belong to the Crown (State).

Peter Pan Statue

Author J.M. Barrie used Kensington Gardens for inspiration to create the character of Peter Pan in 1902. The story of Peter Pan tells the adventures of a boy who can fly and never grows up. He is the leader of a gang called the Lost Boys on the island of Neverland. He is accompanied by a fairy named Tinker Bell.

Count the elves around Elfin Oak, a sculpture made from the trunk of an oak tree.

Captain the pirate ship at the Diana Memorial Playground.

Be dazzled by the bright gold statue at the Albert Memorial.

Funky Fact

Speakers' Corner is a public area, where people have tradition-ally come to loudly debate anything they want to.

History Bits

King Henry VIII created this park in 1536 so he could hunt deer and wild boar. Today celebrations, concerts, demonstrations, festivals, and sports activities all take place here.

Dip your hand in the water at the Princess Diana Memorial Fountain.

You Could...

Visit the Holocaust Memorial.

Go boating
on the Serpentine lake.

Visit the 7 July
Memorial.

Ready Money Drinking Fountain gets its odd name from the nickname of Sir Cowasjee Jehangir, a wealthy businessman from Mumbai, India, who donated it in 1869.

History Bits

Regent's Park was originally created as a hunting ground by King Henry VIII. It opened to the public as a park in 1835 and is sometimes used as a movie set.

Listen to music played on the bandstand.

Rent a boat or pedalo on the lake.

You Could...

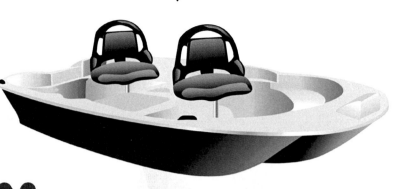

Become a zookeeper for a day at London Zoo.

Find the boy and frog statue in Queen Mary's Garden.

ZOO

More London Adventures

See the Egyptian mummies at the British Museum.

Meet the dinosaurs at the Natural History Museum.

See London from the top of a double-decker bus.

Visit the under-ground bunker and operations room at Churchill's War Rooms.

Even More London Adventures

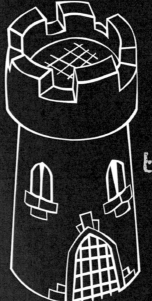

Scream at London's scary history at the London Dungeon.

Have your photo taken with your favorite famous person in Madame Tussauds Waxworks Museum.

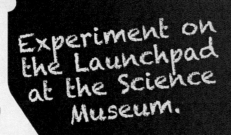

Experiment on the Launchpad at the Science Museum.

Find a painting you like at Tate Britain or Tate Modern.

Legend says King James I gave his wife Anne a house (the Queen's House) as an apology for swearing at her in public after she shot one of his favorite hunting dogs by mistake in 1614.

History Bits

Greenwich is famous for its history and inventions relating to the sea, ships, the sky, and the stars. The Royal Observatory was founded in 1675 and played a key role in astronomy and navigation for ships.

Explore how we tell time and the importance of time zones across the world.

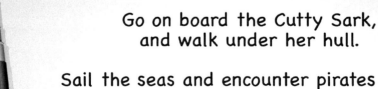

Go on board the Cutty Sark, and walk under her hull.

Sail the seas and encounter pirates at the National Maritime Museum.

Stand on the Prime Meridian, where east meets west, with one foot in each hemisphere (a hemisphere is one half of the world).

Touch a 4.5 billion-year-old meteorite.

Travel across the universe to distant galaxies at the Planetarium.

Food Fun

Find out what these traditional British foods with unusual names are.

- [ ] 1. Bangers and mash
- [ ] 2. Fish fingers and chips
- [ ] 3. Shepherd's pie
- [ ] 4. Toad in the hole
- [ ] 5. Bubble and squeak
- [ ] 6. Crumpets
- [ ] 7. Knickerbocker glory
- [ ] 8. Eton mess
- [ ] 9. Apple crumble with custard

Checkmark the ones you tried.

London **My** Story

Write It Down

These are my favorite memories from London!

Answers to Quick Quizzes ✓

Hello, London!
1) a-The Tube 2) a-Red 3) b-A double-decker 4) b-Black

Buckingham Palace
1) a-Bow or curtsy 2) c-Victoria 3) b-St. James's

Westminster Abbey
1) b-The Last Supper 2) b-A mosaic floor 3) a-Octagonal

Houses of Parliament and Parliament square
1) Winston Churchill 2) Abraham Lincoln 3) Mahatma Gandhi 4) Nelson Mandela

Horse Guards and Whitehall
1) c-The Prime Minister 2) a-Clothing 3) b-The reins 4) a-A monument

St. Paul's Cathedral
1) a-Tombs 2) c-A Painting 3) a-Bells

Trafalgar Square
1) a-A battle 2) c-Arm 3) b-A church

Along the Thames Quiz
1) c-Cleopatra 2) b-To prevent flooding in London 3) c-A World War II warship 4) a-Pedestrians 5) b-Seven

Tower of London
1) c-Executions 2) b-To be seen easily 3) c-Six

Shakespeare's Globe Theatre
1) b-A poet 2) a-Stand 3) c-Twenty

Food Fun
1) Sausages and mashed potatoes 2) Rectangles of fried fish with fries 3) Minced beef in a pie with mashed potato topping 4) Sausages in a batter served with gravy (similar to pigs in a blanket) 5) Leftover vegetables mashed together and fried 6) Similar to English muffins 7) Ice cream sundae 8) Meringues, cream, and fruit 9) Apple crust with a thick, creamy sauce